The Giving Tree of the Desert

The tale of a saguaro cactus and its nurse tree

Written by Danielle Fradette

Illustrated by Tais Lemos

Special thank you to Don Swann with the United States National Park Service

Print ISBN#: 979-8-9856815-0-5

E-Book ISBN#: 979-8-9856815-1-2

Library of Congress Control Number: 2022902457

To purchase additional copies or access supplemental resources visit www.DanielleFradette.com

Published by Common Ground Mentoring

Tucson, AZ

1st Edition

To those who give so others can grow.

Once there was a palo verde tree...
and he loved a little saguaro.

Since she was a tiny black seed
snuggled up close under his branches,
he watched over her...

protecting her from hungry insects
who love to nibble on seeds.

And when the monsoon rains came,
his sturdy roots protected her from the
fast-moving water.

They spent their days together, watching the life of the desert around them.

The saguaro loved the palo verde and the palo verde was happy.

Time went by and the saguaro
grew in its own, slow way.

The palo verde
grew older too.

But, he was still
able to protect her.

When it was too hot under the desert sun, he kept her cool.

When it was too cold during the winter nights, he kept her warm.

When hikers came wearing their big boots, his vast branches saved her from their crushing steps.

When the pocket mice came to feast,
he protected her from
their hungry bellies.

Time went by
and the saguaro grew taller,
her roots spread further,

and the palo verde
grew older too.

One day, while passing time under the
bright shining sun, the saguaro said to
the palo verde, "It is so hot!
The sun is so strong!
I wish I had some shade."

The palo verde sighed,
"You have grown so tall,
I am not able to shade you
from the desert sun like I once did.
But here, take my water,
let it cool you and fill you up."

So the saguaro did.
And she swelled with
happiness (and water)
in the dry desert heat.
The palo verde was happy too.

One day she said to the palo verde
"I'm just so hungry!
Growing tall is hard work."
The palo verde said to the saguaro,
"Here, take the nutrients from the soil,
 I am not growing tall.
Take it and you will be strong."

So the saguaro did and she grew taller.
The palo verde was happy.

Time went by.
The saguaro began to grow arms.
The palo verde grew even older.

Now, when hikers came wearing their big boots,
they took pictures of her proud arms reaching
towards the sun and the flowers on her crown.

Now, when a curious javelina came poking around her, her sharp spines scared it away.

Now, when the monsoon storms came roaring in, her roots held strong into the earth.

"You don't need my protection anymore,"
said the old palo verde.
"But I do need your company,"
said the saguaro.
The palo verde was happy.

Time went by and the saguaro's arms
grew heavy.
The palo verde was so very very old.

"My arms have grown too heavy to
hold. I fear I may fall over."

"My Dear," said the ancient palo verde,
"rest your arms on my limbs and I will
hold you up." So she did.

The saguaro was happy
and so was the palo verde.

The End

facts

- A nurse tree is not always a Palo Verde. Mesquite trees, ironwoods, and other desert plants can also be a nurse tree.

- Saguaros depend on nurse trees for the first 10-20 years of their life until they are big enough to hold the water they need for desert survival.

- Nurse trees add nutrients to the soil around them which other desert plants need to grow.

- In the summer, the canopy of the nurse tree shades the saguaro from the dry heat that can cause it to lose water.

- Nurse trees have deep roots that reach way down into the ground. Saguaros have very shallow roots and can't reach deep water. Saguaros get extra water from their nurse tree as it draws water up from far below the surface.

Be a Desert Protector

The long, slow lives of the Saguaro Cacti can help us to think about the impact we have on the desert and the world. Time moves slowly in nature. What we do today, the planet has to live with after we are gone. Let's live in the desert in a way that allows the people who come after us to enjoy it as we do.

Here are some things you can do to be a Desert Protector:

- Use water wisely. There is not a lot of water in the desert. The animals and plants that live here with us need water just as much as we do.

- Stay on the trails when you go hiking. Some plants like Saguaros are very tiny and can be hard to see. By staying on nature trails we can help make sure we do not step on them.

- Plant native plants in your yard. This saves water and helps the animals that live here.

- Remove buffel grass. Buffel grass is not native to the Sonoran Desert. It can spread fire long distances and destroy the desert plants that would otherwise not have to worry about fire.

For supplemental resources, activities, and games,
visit www.DanielleFradette.com

Made in United States
Troutdale, OR
10/11/2024

23671012R00024